Mystery Mob
and the
Creepy Castle

Roger Hurn

Illustrated by
Stik

Rising Stars UK Ltd.
22 Grafton Street, London W1S 4EX
www.risingstars-uk.com

The right of Roger Hurn to be identified as the author of this work
has been asserted by him in accordance with the Copyright,
Design and Patents Act 1988.

Published 2007

Cover design: Button plc
Illustrator: Stik, Bill Greenhead for Illustration
Text design and typesetting: Andy Wilson
Publisher: Gill Budgell
Publishing manager: Sasha Morton
Editor: Catherine Baker
Series consultant: Cliff Moon

British Library Cataloguing in Publication Data.
A CIP record for this book is available from the British Library

ISBN: 978-1-84680-227-0

Printed in the UK by CPI Bookmarque, Croydon, CR0 4TD

Mixed Sources
Product group from well-managed
forests and other controlled sources
www.fsc.org Cert no. TT-COC-002227
© 1996 Forest Stewardship Council
FSC

Contents

Meet the Mystery Mob

Name:

Gummy

FYI: Gummy hasn't got much brain – and even fewer teeth.

Loves: Soup.

Hates: Toffee chews.

Fact: The brightest thing about him is his shirt.

Name:

Lee

FYI: If Lee was any cooler he'd be a cucumber.

Loves: Hip-hop.

Hates: Hopscotch.

Fact: He has his own designer label (which he peeled off a tin).

Name:

Rob

FYI: Rob lives in his own world – he's just visiting planet Earth.

Loves: Daydreaming.

Hates: Nightmares.

Fact: Rob always does his homework – he just forgets to write it down.

Name:

Dwayne

FYI: Dwayne is smarter than a tree full of owls.

Loves: Anything complicated.

Hates: Join-the-dots books.

Fact: If he was any brighter you could use him as a floodlight at football matches.

Name:

FYI: Chet is as brave as a lion with steel jaws.

Loves: Having adventures.

Hates: Knitting.

Fact: He's as tough as the chicken his granny cooks for his tea.

Name:

FYI: Adi is as happy as a football fan with tickets to the big match.

Loves: Telling jokes.

Hates: Moaning minnies.

Fact: He knows more jokes than a jumbo joke book.

Getting the Creeps

The Mystery Mob are standing outside
a dark and gloomy old castle.
A wooden drawbridge leads across
a misty moat. It is a really spooky place.

Rob   Remind me – why did we
come here for our holiday?

Chet   Because it's totally cool
to stay in an old castle.

Gummy   But this place
is just soooo creepy.

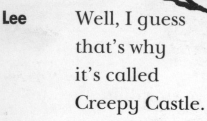

Lee   Well, I guess that's why it's called Creepy Castle.

Adi   And I guess that's why it's soooo cheap to stay here.

Dwayne   Actually, it's called Creepy Castle because that's the name of the family that owns it – the Creepys. They've lived here for hundreds of years.

Gummy   Wow! They must be pretty old then.

Dwayne   Doh!

Gummy   Oh right. I get it. You mean
there's always been a Creepy
family living in the castle.

Just then, a young woman walks up to
the Mystery Mob. She smiles at the boys.
She says her name is Suzi Creepy.
She is the last of the Creepy family,
and this makes her the owner of the castle.

Lee   Awesome!

Rob   It must be so cool to have your own castle.

Chet   And it's really kind of you to rent it out so kids like us can come and stay.

Dwayne   Yes, it gives us a chance to learn all about history.

Gummy   No. It gives us a chance to play at being knights in armour – for real!

Suzi looks sad.

Suzi   I'm glad you like the castle.
But I'm going to have to sell it.
The money I make from renting
it out won't pay the repair bills.
And I'm broke.

Adi   No way! You must be mega-rich
to live in a place like this.

But Suzi shakes her head.

Suzi   No, it's true – I really am broke.
Long ago, there was a war.
Old Sir Crawley Creepy hid
the family treasure. He wanted
to keep it safe from his enemies.
But he died without telling
anyone where he had hidden
the treasure. Ever since then
my family has been poor.

Adi   That's a real hard-luck story.

Dwayne Yes, but if we find the treasure for you, Suzi, you can pay the bills.

Chet   And you won't have to sell the castle.

Gummy Cool! Your worries are over, Suzi. The Mystery Mob is on the case!

The boys search high and low
all over the castle for the treasure.

Lee It's no good. We're all tired and
it's getting too dark to see.

Rob So, let's call it a day.

Adi No, let's call it a knight!

Mystery Mob

(groaning) Goodnight, Adi.

The boys head off to bed.

A Sleepless Knight

Rob and Lee are fast asleep in their room.
Rob wakes up. Something's wrong. The
room is very cold. He sits up and shivers.

Rob   Wake up, Lee!

Lee   (sleepily) No, I don't want to.
It's the middle of the night and
I'm having a brilliant dream.
I'm just about to score
the winning goal for City.

Rob   Forget football. There's a ghost in the room with us!

Lee   Huh? Look, I may be dreaming – but I think you're having a nightmare.

Rob   No I'm not. I'm wide awake. There is a ghost – and he's at the end of my bed.

Lee	Do you mean that bloke who's all dressed up like someone from the olden days?
Rob	So you *can* see him.
Lee	Sort of. I can certainly see right through him.
Rob	That proves he's a ghost.
Lee	Right. But ghosts are supposed to be scary.

Rob   That works for me. I *am* scared.
Look, I'm shaking like a jelly on
a snowboard.

Lee   No, you're just shivering because
it's freezing cold in here.

Rob   Oh – that's all right then.
Go away, Mr Ghost.
You don't frighten us.

Lee   Shut up, Rob. Look at his face.
You're making him cross!
And we really don't need
a sulky spook on our case.

Rob   (gulping) Look! He's pointing his long, thin, bony finger at us. Arghhh! Why's he doing that?

Lee   I think he wants us to follow him.

Rob But where to? Oh please, don't let it be to the graveyard!

Lee Well, we'll never know unless
we go after him, will we?
Oh, come on, you loser!
Stop hiding under the blanket.
We've got a real live ghost here!

Rob Yes, but I prefer ghosts when they stay dead.

The ghost turns and walks through the wall. Then he sticks his head back through the wall. He nods as he sees the boys coming after him.

Rob   Er … how are we going to walk through the wall?

Lee   We're not. We're going to open the door. The ghost will be waiting for us out in the corridor.

Rob   I knew that.

Creepy Crawley

The ghost floats through the castle.
He drifts over the drawbridge.
The moon is half hidden by
dark clouds. Rob and Lee
hurry after him.

Rob   Where do you think the ghost is
taking us?

Lee	To the *dead centre* of the castle grounds.
Rob	Where's that?
Lee	The graveyard.
Rob	That's not funny.
Lee	I'm not joking. Look. The ghost's stopped next to that old gravestone. He's pointing at it. I think he wants us to read what it says.

The boys walk up to the gravestone.

Rob   Yikes! It says: 'Here lies Sir Crawley Creepy. RIP.'

Lee   So this must be the ghost of Sir Crawley Creepy.

Rob   He's nodding his head. Oh, please don't let it fall off! I really don't want to see him put it under his arm!

Lee   Hey, it was Sir Crawley Creepy who hid the treasure, wasn't it?

Rob   That's right, and now he's smiling. But why? It says RIP, but he's not exactly resting in peace.

Lee   Maybe he's going to show us where he hid the treasure so we can give it to Suzi and save the castle.

The ghost jumps up and down with excitement.

Rob   You've scored a bull's eye! That's the answer. But I don't get it. Why us? Why doesn't he just show Suzi?

Lee   Maybe she can't see him.

Rob   Right! And I can – so I guess I must be like a medium.

Lee   No, I'd say you're more a small than a medium.

Rob   Ha! Ha! You're *so* not funny.
             Is he, Sir Crawley?

But the ghost says nothing. He turns and
glides away.

Rob   Oi! Where's he off to now?

Lee   I've got no idea. Hang on,
             Sir Crawley. Wait for us.

4

Creepy Dungeon

Sir Crawley Creepy takes the boys
back into the castle. He leads them
down to a dark dungeon. He stops
outside the door of a tiny cell.
A skeleton is chained to the wall.
An old rusty key is in the lock.

Rob   I'm not going into that cell.

Lee   Why not?

Rob   For starters – there's a skeleton
there. What if he's got a bone to
pick with us?

Lee   Don't be daft. It's only a plastic
skeleton. Come on.

The lads step inside the cell. It is smelly and damp. The ghost points to a big pile of straw in one corner.

Rob   What's he trying to tell us?

Lee   I've got no idea. Maybe the treasure is under the straw.

Rob   Then what are we waiting for? Let's shift it. Oh yuk!

Lee   What's up?

Rob   This straw is full of rat poo!
Now I've got it all over me.

Lee   Shame. But it could have been
worse.

Rob   How come?

Lee   I could've got it all over me.
Hey – come and look at this.

Rob What is it?

Lee A metal ring set in the stone floor.
I'm going to give it a tug. I think
the treasure is hidden under it.

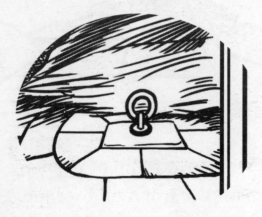

Dead End

Lee pulls on the ring but it won't budge.
The ghost frowns and then points at Rob.

Rob   I think he wants me to help you.

Lee   Well, come on then. Grab hold of
the ring and we'll both pull as
hard as we can.

Rob   I've got it. One … two … three …
heave!

The boys pull hard. Then, suddenly, the stone with the ring in it comes up from the floor. Both boys fall back into the pile of mucky straw.

Lee   Eeuurgh! I've got rat poo on *me* now.

Rob   It looks good on you – it's SO your colour! Now I'm going to see what's in that hole.

Rob crawls over to the hole in the floor.
He looks into it. He reaches in and pulls
out a wooden box.

Rob   Right, let's see what we've got in
            here. I'll just flip the catch like so
            and, hey presto, it's open.
            Oh Lee, check this out.

Lee   Wow, the treasure is like a
rainbow trapped in a box.
It must be worth a fortune.

Rob   Suzi's going to be well happy.
Now she won't have to sell the
castle. It can stay in the Creepy
family forever. Thanks for this,
Sir Crawley. Hey, he's gone.

Lee   Never mind. He did what he came to do. He showed us where he'd hidden the treasure. Mind you, it's just as well he did.

Rob   Why's that?

Lee   Because we didn't have a *ghost* of a chance of finding it without him!

About the author

Roger Hurn has:

 been an actor in 'The Exploding Trouser Company'

 played bass guitar in a rock band

been given the title Malam Oga (wise teacher, big boss!) while on a storytelling trip to Africa.

Now he's a writer, and he hopes you like reading about the Mystery Mob as much as he likes writing about them.

Castles quiz

Questions

1 What is a knight?

2 What is a moat?

3 What games did people play in castles in the olden days?

4 What is a drawbridge?

5 Why were people who lived in castles good at history?

6 Why didn't people who lived in castles wash very often?

7 What was the name given to the castle toilet?

8 What do you call a person locked up in a castle dungeon?

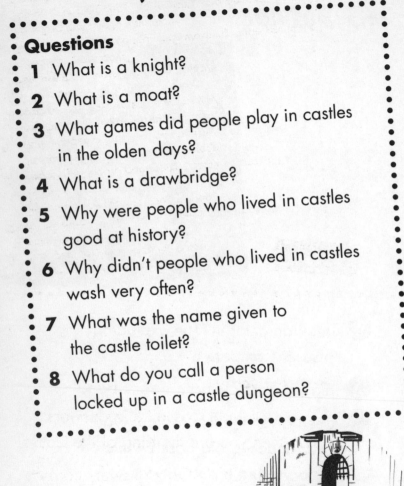

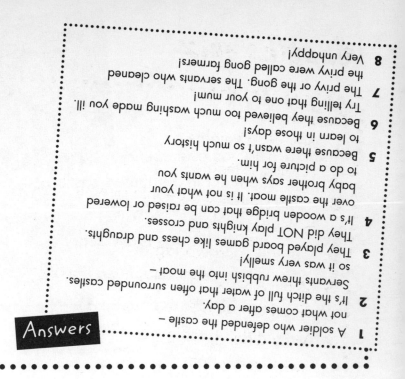

Answers

1 A soldier who defended the castle –
not what comes after a day.

2 It's the ditch full of water that often surrounded castles.
Servants threw rubbish into the moat –
so it was very smelly!

3 They played board games like chess and draughts.
They did NOT play knights and crosses.

4 It's a wooden bridge that can be raised or lowered
over the castle moat. It is not what your
baby brother says when he wants you
to do a picture for him.

5 Because there wasn't so much history
to learn in those days!

6 Because they believed too much washing made you ill.
Try telling that one to your mum!

7 The privy or the gong. The servants who cleaned
the privy were called gong farmers!

8 Very unhappy!

How did you score?

🖐 If you got all eight Castle Quiz answers
correct, then you are the King of the Castle!

🖐 If you got six Castle Quiz answers correct,
then you're ready to be a knight for a day.

🖐 If you got fewer than four Castle Quiz
answers correct, then you're the dirty rascal!

When I was a kid

Question Did you ever spend
the night in a haunted castle
when you were a kid?

Roger Yes, and it was really scary.

Question Why? What happened?

Roger A coffin chased me all over the castle.

Question What did you do?

Roger I ran away as fast as I could,
but everywhere I went
the coffin kept coming after me.

Question That's terrible. How did you escape?

Roger I ran into the bathroom,
grabbed a bottle of cough syrup
from a cupboard
and threw it at the coffin.

Question What happened?

Roger The coffin finally stopped!

Adi's favourite knight joke

What time is it when a knight looks at his belly button?

The middle of the knight!

How to be a knight

First you have to go to knight school.

*If your last name is Render, change it!
You'll never win a battle if you're called
Sir Render!*

It's dark inside a castle so take
a knight-light with you.

*Make sure you always have a tin opener
handy in case you get stuck
in your suit of armour.*

*When you choose your horse
make sure it's well behaved
and not a knight mare.*

Don't fall into the moat
wearing your armour. If you do,
everyone will call you 'Rusty'.

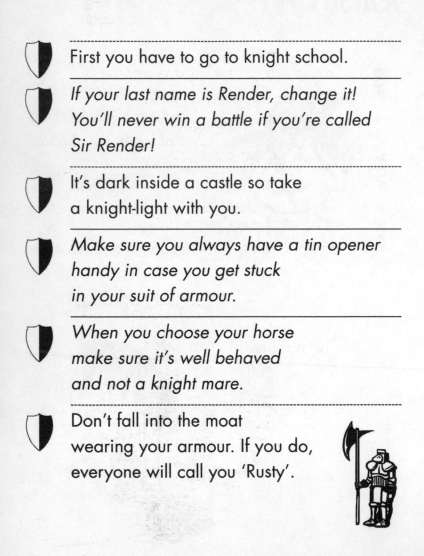

 Never forget that dragons sleep during the day. They do this so they can fight knights.

 The best place to meet other knights is in a knight club.

 Get used to your mum saying, "Nighty knight," when you go to bed.

Five freaky 'facts' about creepy castles

1   Muncaster Castle claims to have more ghosts than any other castle in Britain. Lots of tales are told of doors opening all by themselves and rooms going cold for no reason!

2   People say the ghost of a 'Grey Lady' walks the walls of Ruthin Castle in Wales. She murdered her husband's girlfriend with an axe!

3   Glamis Castle in Scotland has a legend about a secret room hidden within its walls. This secret room is supposed to be the home of a monster!

4   Everybody who lived in Cainhoe Castle, in England, died at the same time from the Black Death. It wasn't till much later that their bodies were found by a passing traveller. How creepy is that?

5   The Tower of London is said to be haunted by King Henry the Eighth's wife, Ann Boleyn. Henry had her head chopped off there – so perhaps she's still looking for it!

Castle lingo

Jester A clown who entertained the lord of the castle by telling jokes and doing tricks. If his jokes weren't funny he had 'jester second' to escape before he was thrown into the dungeon!

Keep A large tower. If you are the lord of the castle you get to keep the keep.

Moat A deep ditch filled with water – a kind of old-fashioned outside toilet.

Motte and bailey A type of castle – not United's new strikers.

Murder holes Openings in a castle ceiling. Soldiers dropped heavy rocks or boiling oil through them on to the heads of anyone who attacked the castle. Don't stand underneath a murder hole – it's a dead end.

Mystery Mob

RISING STARS